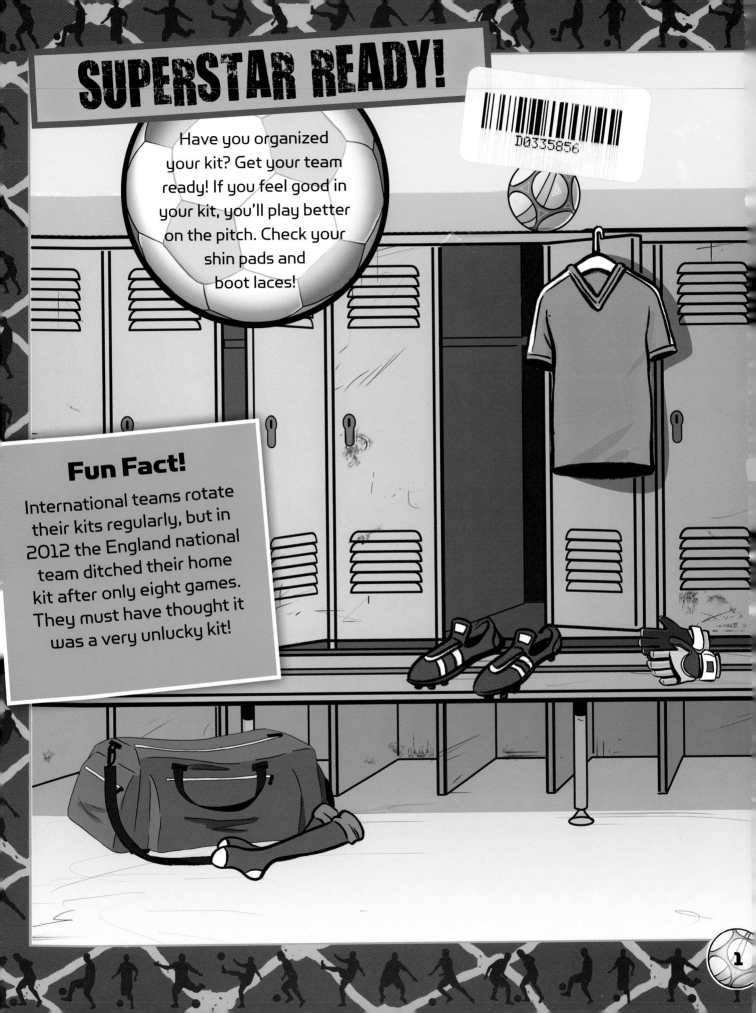

SUPERSTAR READY!

Have you organized your kit? Get your team ready! If you feel good in your kit, you'll play better on the pitch. Check your shin pads and boot laces!

Fun Fact!

International teams rotate their kits regularly, but in 2012 the England national team ditched their home kit after only eight games. They must have thought it was a very unlucky kit!

SUPERSTAR DRIBBLER

- Learn moves at a walking pace before gradually building up speed.

- Dribble through a line of cones using the inside and outside of your boot.

- Get competitive and set up two equal-length cone slaloms. Split players into two relay teams. Each player must dribble in and out of the cones – don't miss any cones out!

TRAINING TIME

Practise your footy skills! Create your scene and check out the superstar skills tips. Prepare for match challenges and don't forget the all-important warm-ups!

Warm-up Checklist

Jogging ☐

Skipping ☐

Running ☐

Knee-lifts ☐

Stretching ☐

TOP TIP

Clean your boots and dry them each time you use them, so you're ready for your next superstar performance!

Superstar Kit

What would your superstar kit look like? Design it here!

FOOTY PRACTICE

Once you've practised passing, tackling and cool tricks and flicks with your team-mates, you'll be ready for a superstar match performance!

Stepover

1) Whilst dribbling, plant to the side of the ball.

2) Make an exaggerate around the front of t

3) Push the ball in the defender's aim, ther

TOP BALL CONTROL

- Use firm control to make a good first pass or push the ball into a space ahead of you. As you go to kick the ball, keep firm the part of your body that will strike the ball back.

- For a sidefoot cushion, line yourself up with the ball, lift your leg and turn your ankle so that the side of your foot is facing the ball. Keep your foot still and let the ball roll onto it, or move your foot towards the ball.

Super Sprinter

1) Start on the goal line and sprint for 3 seconds.

2) Jog back, then sprint for 5 seconds.

3) Jog back, then sprint for 10 seconds.

4) Repeat three times!

TOP TRICKS

Practise these tricks by yourself and with friends.

...one foot

... swing of your other foot ... e ball to the other side.

... pposite direction to the ... swerve past them.

Dragback

1) Start by shaping to play the ball in the direction you are heading.
2) Stop the ball with the sole of your boot.
3) Use the sole to drag the ball backwards as you pivot on your other foot, turning to face a different direction.
4) Sprint away!

My Favourite Superstar Tricks

1) _____

2) _____

3) _____

FREE-KICK!

Your team has started the match well and has been awarded a free-kick! Create your scene as the ball flies over the wall of players, then check out the superstar tips and facts!

★ ★ ★ ★ ★

Free-kick Techniques

- Bend the ball round the edge of the wall.

- Loop the ball up and over towards goal.

- Shape to shoot, but actually roll the ball to a team-mate who is at an angle to shoot without the wall blocking their attempt.

TACKLING TIP

Only make a tackle when you know you have defensive cover behind you. Stay on your feet and don't shy away! There may be body contact with the opposition, but if you've timed your tackle well, you won't get hurt.

Practice Checklist

Tick these off when you and your mates have practised them.

Passing ☐

Tackling ☐

Tricks and flicks ☐

Headers ☐

Volleys ☐

Free-kicks ☐

Corners ☐

Page 1

3 5 6 8

Pages 4–5

Pages 6–7

Pages 8–9

Pages 10–11

Pages 10–11

Page 12

age 12

Inside back cover

TOP TEAM

TOURNAMENT WINNERS

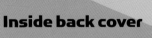

TEAM TALK

Time for a half-time pep talk! Become the manager and place your own player formation on the board, using your stickers. Then fill the scene as your team discusses top tactics for the second-half!

Player Tips

- Rest. Catch your breath – you're more likely to take in the manager's comments.

- Rehydrate. Drink fluids to regain your strength.

- Give the manager any second-half suggestions. Use your knowledge of the game!

TOP TIP

Forming a wall at free-kicks narrows the space the striker can shoot into. The goalkeeper will position the wall to block one side, then stand in the remaining part of the goal, giving them a better chance of saving the shot!

MANAGER TIPS

- Inspire your players – remind them how important the game is.
- Get your players' confidence back on track if they're losing.
- Give feedback on the technical, tactical and physical aspects of the first-half.

If your team is not doing well, boost morale and get the players motivated at half-time – it could mean the difference between pulling off a win instead of a draw!

TOP TIP

When you're about to shoot, think about where the keeper can easily save it. You could put it in the top corner where the goalie can't reach, kick it into the opposite corner or just power it along the ground.

GOAL!!!

Your team's tactics have won them the championship and the fans are going wild! Create your scene as the players celebrate their superstar performance!

Top Tactics

Once your goalkeeper is in place on the board, choose the formation. You could go defensive and play three centre backs, or pick an attacking line-up with three strikers. It's your decision—choose one of these formations, or think up your own.

4-4-2
4-3-3
4-2-4
3-5-2
4-1-3-1-1

WINNERS!!!

The fans have gone mad for their footy heroes! Fill this celebratory scene with your stickers as the players show off their shining superstar trophy.

PER SCORER!

rers guess where the ball will fall
et into position as early as possible
not. So remember to always play
ead up and keep scanning the game!

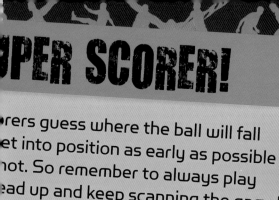

Top Five Match Moments

1) _____
_____
2) _____
_____
3) _____
_____
4) _____
_____
5) _____
_____

SU

Top goalsc
and try to g
to make a s
with your h

Headliners!

The cameras are capturing your team's success! Come up with a catchy headline that will appear in the press the next day.

Winning Chant

The fans are enjoying your victory!
Write a catchy footy chant here.

_____

_____

_____

_____